Mapping
the
Yoniverse

with
Samantha Zipporah

An Anatomy Coloring Book
Illustrated by Casandra Johns

Illustrated by Casandra Johns, House of Hands

Cover Art by Amy Willis

ISBN 978-1-64633-283-0

"The possession of
knowledge does
not kill the sense of
wonder & mystery.

There is always
more mystery."

Anaïs Nin

TABLE OF CONTENTS

ACKNOWLEDGMENTS.............................7

A NOTE ABOUT TERMINOLOGY 8

PART 1

PHYSICAL ANATOMY...........................9

VULVA & EXTERNAL GENITALIA 10

RUGEA 14

INTERNAL CLITORIS...........................16

INTERNAL ORGANS 19

LAYERS OF UTERINE TISSUE....................22

FIMBRIAE..................................24

CONNECTIVE TISSUE.........................25

A NOTE ABOUT VAGINAL FLUIDS & SECRETIONS.....27

GLANDS...................................28

PART 2

SEXUAL ENERGY ANATOMY......................30

UNIFYING PHILOSOPHIES.......................31

TAOISM & THE MICROCOSMIC ORBIT...............32

TANTRA 34

KABBALAH 36

RESOURCES 39

ABOUT THE AUTHOR.........................40

ABOUT THE ILLUSTRATOR......................40

INDEX.....................................41

ACKNOWLEDGMENTS

Carol Downer

Suzann Gage

The Federation of Feminist Women's Health Centers

Sherri Winston

Ellen Heed

Mantak Chia

My ancestors & the process of healing intergenerational womb-trauma

Amy Willis

Casandra Johns

Katharine Vogel

Tirzah Firestone

Evelin Dacker

A NOTE ABOUT TERMINOLOGY

Yoni: Appreciation, Not Appropriation

"Yoni" is a Sanskrit word that translates as "womb," "uterus," "vagina," "vulva," "abode," or "source." Sanskrit is about 3,500 years old & from India. It is the language of many religious Hindu, Buddhist, & Jainist texts. I humbly acknowledge the lineage & history of the word Yoni, for which there is no equivalent in the English language. It is with a clear intention of appreciation rather than appropriation that I playfully combine of the word "yoni" & "universe" to express the vastness of this part of human anatomy both physically & energetically.

Description, Not Eponym

Throughout this offering you will find descriptive terms like "egg tube" replacing formal eponyms like "fallopian tube." *Eponyms* are nouns named for the person who discovered or invented them. Inspired by the women who wrote "A New View of A Woman's Body" & other activist linguists, I reject the inherent misogyny of calling my body parts by the names of old white dudes who "discovered" them. Using descriptive terms is a practical way to improve both comprehension & reclamation of our bodies.

Anatomy, Not Gender

Anatomy does not define gender or sexual identity. I strive to make my work accessible to & inclusive of diverse identities by referring to specific body parts & their physiologic processes without assuming the gender or sexual preference of the person to whom the body or process belongs. Also, some people have intersex genitals, & some people do not identify with the sex or gender they were assigned at birth. I use the terms Assigned Female at Birth (AFAB) & Assigned Male at Birth (AMAB) to acknowledge these realities. At the time of publishing this book these terms seemed the most respectful & inclusive option available. Language is constantly evolving, & I look forward to participating in the evolution of both our culture & its terminology to celebrate & describe diverse bodies & identities.

Pregnancy Release

Not all pregnancies end in birth. I use the term "pregnancy release" to normalize the processes of birth, miscarriage, abortion, & stillbirth & acknowledge their similarities. All pregnancy experiences have a phase of holding, release, & postpartum that deserve education, supportive community, & care.

Part 1

PHYSICAL ANATOMY

VULVA & EXTERNAL GENITALIA

The genitalia visible from the outside of somebody Assigned Female At Birth (AFAB) is called the vulva. Vulvas come in many different colors, shapes, & sizes. Their flesh comes in pale pink, purple, grey, brown, magenta, red, & any number of other variations & combinations! Some have long lips, others have short. Some are smooth, others are frilly & ruffly. Many pairs of labia are asymmetrical, & some have a multi-inch long clitoris peeking out of them. All these variations are perfectly normal & healthy. Indeed, no two vulvas are alike!

Rather than worrying if a vulva is "normal," learn to appreciate its unique beauty & all of the pleasure it has in store.

Inner lips

Outer lips

Pubic Mound

Clitoral Head

Clitoral Hood

Clitoral Shaft

Vaginal Opening

Vestibule

Urethral Opening

Perineum

Anus

1. Inner Lips

The Latin & clinical terminology for these lovelies is *labia minora*. The inner labia usually extend from the head of the clitoris around either side of the urethral & vaginal openings. In some people the inner labia are completely concealed within the outer labia, while in others they protrude out. Inner labia are made up of fancy erectile tissue which becomes engorged during full sexual arousal.

2. Outer Lips

The outer lips grace either side of the vaginal opening just outside of the inner lips. The clinical term for these lips, *labia majora*, is Latin for larger lips. However, some vulvas have inner lips that are actually larger than the outer ones.

3. Pubic Mound

The pubic mound, also known as the *mons pubis* or *mons venus* (after the Roman goddess of love) is a soft mound of fatty tissue that sits atop the pubic bone. This fleshy mound contains many nerves & at puberty often becomes covered with pubic hair. It is worth noting that the nerves of a fully engorged clitoris may often be stimulated effectively by placing pressure externally on the pubic mound.

4. Clitoral Head

Aside from the hood, the only part of the clitoris that is visible from the outside is the glans or head. The glans is either tucked under, peaks out, or protrudes out from underneath the clitoral hood. It is by far the most sensitive part of the clitoris, hosting the greatest number of nerve endings per square inch. It is analogous to the glans or head of the penis.

5. Clitoral Hood

The clitoris is covered & protected by a fold of tissue that is part of the inner lips, making up what is called a clitoral hood, or prepuce. This hood is somewhat similar to the foreskin of the penis.

6. Clitoral Shaft

The shaft of the clitoris is hidden from our eyes under the flesh of the pubic mound & the ridge of the pubic bone. In a relaxed state it is approximately one to two inches long & a little over half an inch wide. It contains two spongy erectile bodies of tissue called cavernous bodies, or the corpora cavernosa. This tissue becomes engorged with blood during sexual arousal, increasing the size of the clitoris. The shaft of the clitoris is analogous with the shaft of the penis in the male.

7. Vaginal Opening

The vaginal opening, or in Latin clinical terms, *introitus*, is the narrowest portion of the vagina. It is located at the base of the vestibule. The vaginal opening is rarely visible without spreading the inner lips. The vagina is more commonly an exit than an entrance. The Latin term introitus, which means entrance, is one more way medical terminology subtly centers the other which might penetrate or enter the vagina (such as sexual partners, objects, medical care providers) rather than our own bodies natural processes for which the vaginal opening is an exit (such as discharge, fluids or pregnancies).

8. Vestibule

Vestibule means "hall or lobby adjacent to the entrance of a building." The urethra, the vestibular glands, & the vagina all open adjacent to the vestibule. You can think of the vestibule as the front porch or lobby of all those openings.

9. Urethral Opening

This is what you pee out of! Although its function is not reproductive, the urethra is considered part of the genitalia because of its location. Peeing after sex is important to avoid bacterial infections. The friction & movements of sexual activity can push foreign bacteria into the delicate environment of the urethra, & peeing helps wash them out.

10. Perineum

Between the vulva & the anus is a wonderfully sensitive stretch of skin known as the perineum. Often it has some hair on it, & will respond pleasurably to pressure or stroking during sexual play.

11. Anus

The anus is the very end of our digestive intestinal tract. It's where your poop comes out! The anus contains nerves that are connected to the perineum, clitoris & vagina. With proper lube, relaxation & other thoughtful safety measures, the anus can be source of sexual pleasure.

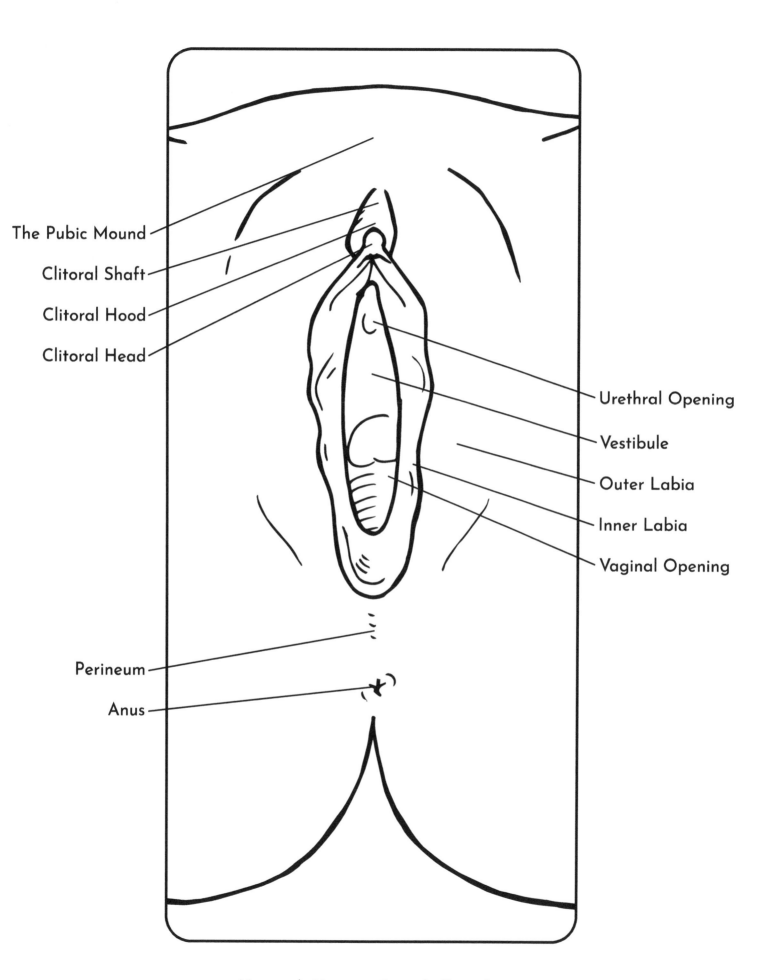

The Pubic Mound

Clitoral Shaft

Clitoral Hood

Clitoral Head

Urethral Opening

Vestibule

Outer Labia

Inner Labia

Vaginal Opening

Perineum

Anus

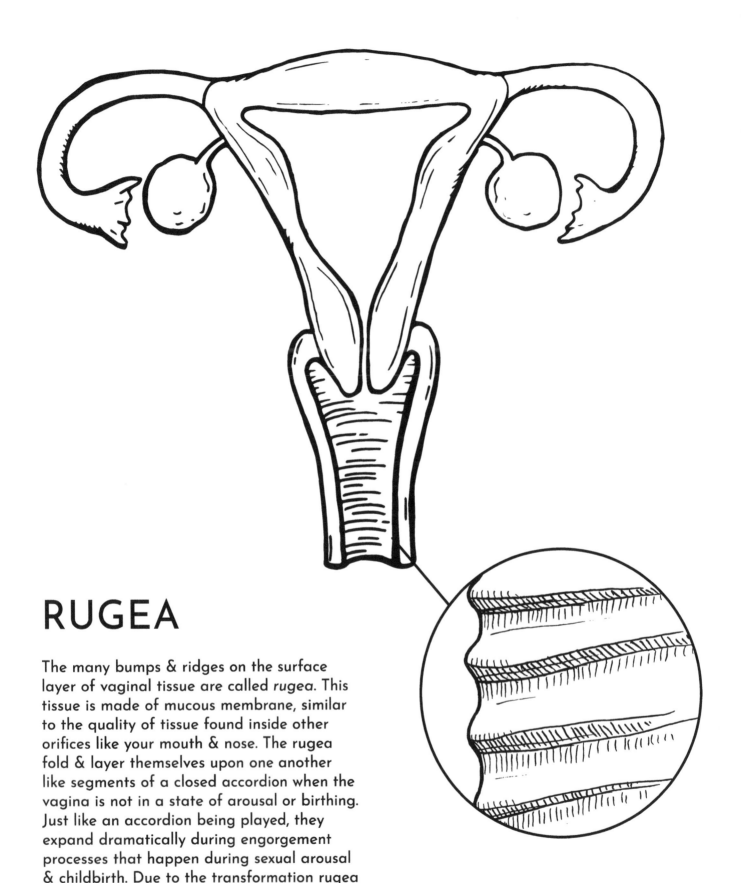

RUGEA

The many bumps & ridges on the surface layer of vaginal tissue are called *rugea*. This tissue is made of mucous membrane, similar to the quality of tissue found inside other orifices like your mouth & nose. The rugea fold & layer themselves upon one another like segments of a closed accordion when the vagina is not in a state of arousal or birthing. Just like an accordion being played, they expand dramatically during engorgement processes that happen during sexual arousal & childbirth. Due to the transformation rugea create when blood flow & engorgement happen, the vagina can expand up to **200%**.

Mapping the Yoniverse ✳ Samantha Zipporah

Relaxed

Aroused!

INTERNAL CLITORIS

The clitoris has many more parts to it than most people realize. It is formed from the same type of erectile tissues that form the penis in AMAB bodies. *On average, inch for inch & pound for pound, AFAB bodies have the same amount of erectile tissue as AMAB do.* Most of it is within the internal structure of the clitoris. There is an abundance of nerve endings throughout the clitoris & in the area around it. Taking the time to explore how your unique clitoris prefers to be stimulated will be rewarding!

Clitoral head

Clitoral shaft

Clitoral legs

Vestibular bulbs

1. The Clitoral Head

Aside from the hood, the only part of the clitoris that can be seen externally is the head. Clinically called the glans, it is either hidden by or sticking out from underneath the clitoral hood (see page 11). The head is by far the most sensitive part of the clitoris, hosting the greatest number of nerve endings per square inch of the human body. Many people do not tolerate or enjoy direct stimulation of the clitoral head, & prefer to be pleasured by stimulating the head *through* the protective layer of its hood.

2. The Clitoral Shaft

The shaft of the clitoris is on average approximately one to two inches long, sometimes up to five. It is usually a little over half an inch wide. It contains two spongy erectile bodies of tissue called cavernous bodies, or the *corpora cavernosa*. This tissue of these erectile bodies becomes engorged with blood during sexual arousal, greatly increasing the size & sensitivity of the clitoris. The tissue that develops into the shaft of a penis in developing fetuses is the same tissue that becomes the clitoral shaft.

3. The Clitoral Legs

The base of the clitoral shaft divides into two legs, or *crura*. Each leg is between two & four inches long. The legs of the clitoris follow below the arch of the pubic bone. The clitoral legs are made of spongy erectile tissue that become engorged & sensitive during sexual arousal.

4. Vestibular Bulbs

The vestibular bulbs, also sometimes called the clitoral bulbs, consist of two masses of spongy erectile tissue on either side of the vestibule. The vestibular bulbs swell with blood during sexual arousal, pressing in on the vaginal opening & making it more snug. The swelling of the vestibular bulbs can create a sensation of gripping or hugging of a penis or any other penetrating object because of the pressure they exert on the walls of the vaginal opening.

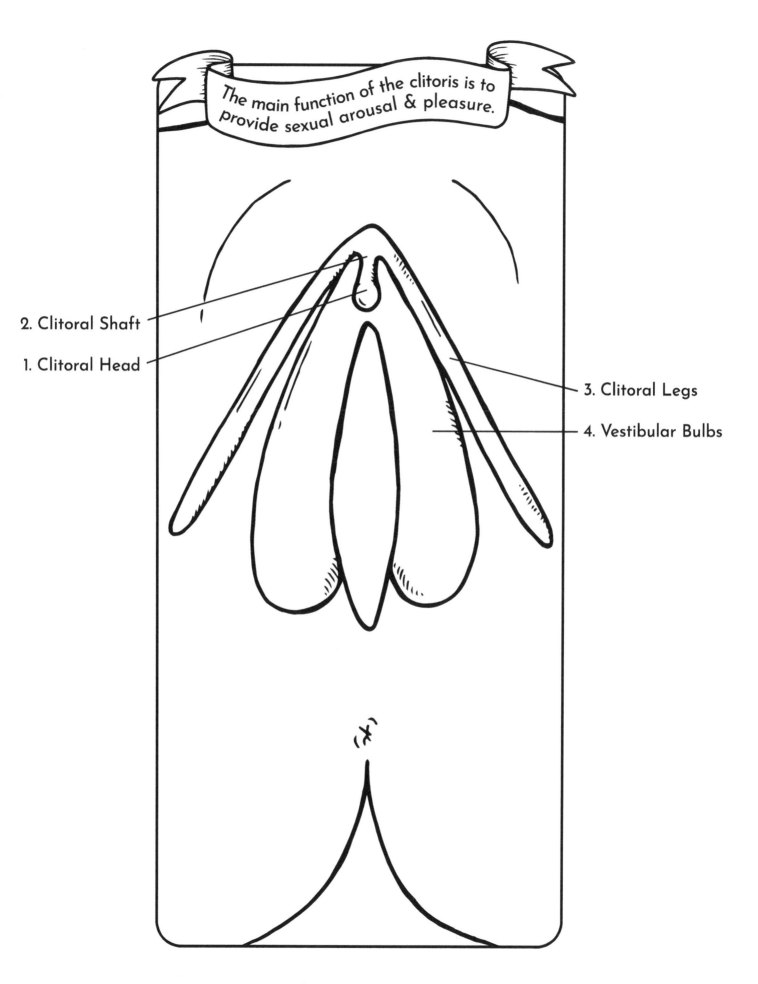

The main function of the clitoris is to provide sexual arousal & pleasure.

2. Clitoral Shaft

1. Clitoral Head

3. Clitoral Legs

4. Vestibular Bulbs

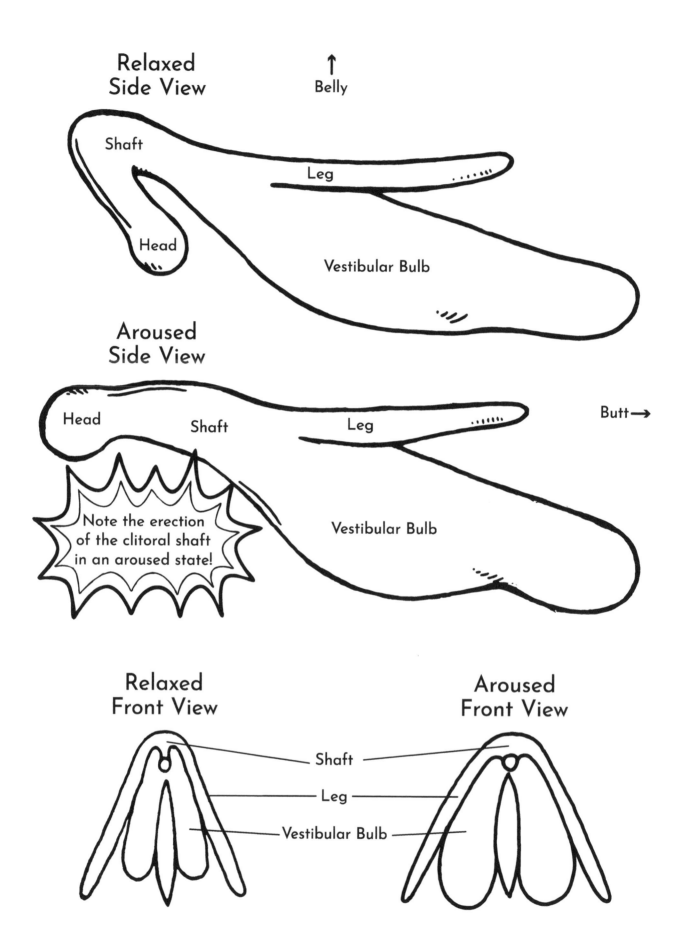

Relaxed
Side View

↑
Belly

Shaft

Leg

Head

Vestibular Bulb

Aroused
Side View

Head

Shaft

Leg

Butt →

Note the erection
of the clitoral shaft
in an aroused state!

Vestibular Bulb

Relaxed
Front View

Aroused
Front View

Shaft

Leg

Vestibular Bulb

INTERNAL ORGANS

Most of the internal AFAB reproductive organs, including the uterus, ovaries, & egg (or fallopian) tubes are impossible to see. With the help of a speculum, flashlight, & a mirror one may get a glance at the vaginal walls & the cervix.

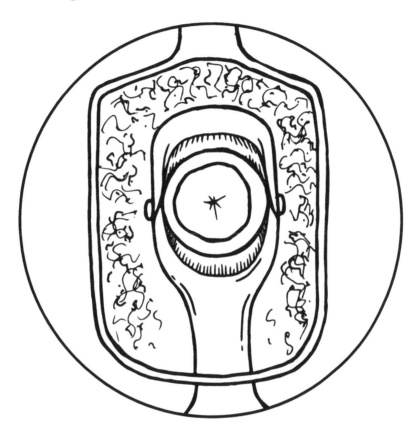

Cervix seen through a speculum

Egg tubes

Uterus

Ovaries

Cervix

Vagina

1. The Egg Tubes

The egg tubes are widely known by their eponym Fallopian. These tubes are about four inches long & their purpose is to provide safe passage for an egg to travel from the ovary to the uterus. Contrary to popular belief, the egg tubes are not connected to the ovaries structurally. Rather, the fringed edges or *fimbriea* that encircle their openings rest just beside the ovary. (see page 24 for more information about fimbriea)

2. The Ovaries

Human eggs are produced & stored in the ovaries. After ovulation happens the empty egg follicle in the ovary becomes an endocrine gland that produce important hormones. People generally have two ovaries, but some are born with only one or none. During their active years, healthy ovaries are about the size & shape of almonds & alternate the task of maturing & releasing an egg about once a month. The ovaries of people who take hormonal birth control stop working as endocrine glands because they stop ovulating, & shrink to about 50% their normal size.

3. The Uterus

The uterus, also referred to sometimes as the womb, is about the size & shape of a small pear when not pregnant. This organ is credited with being the 5th strongest muscle in the human body. The uterus is an average of 3 to 4 inches long, & 2.5 inches wide during our reproductive years while not pregnant. The uterus can grow up to 500 times its non pregnant size during a pregnancy.

4. The Cervix

The cervix is the tip of the uterus. Cervix means "neck." The opening in the center of the cervix is called the cervical 'os'. It is through the cervical os that sperm can enter the uterus. This is also where menstrual blood or pregnancy exits the uterus.

5. The Vagina

The vagina is made up of extremely expandable tissue which forms a canal, about four inches long. It is considered a "potential space" because most of the time the walls of the vagina rest against each other. The vagina expands exponentially during high states of arousal & childbirth. The third of the vagina closest to its opening is full of ridges called rugea (See page 14) & has more nerve endings than the rest of the vagina, making it the most sensitive portion. The tissue of the inner two-thirds of the vagina is much smoother. The inner two thirds are less sensitive to touch, friction, or vibration, but still responsive to pressure.

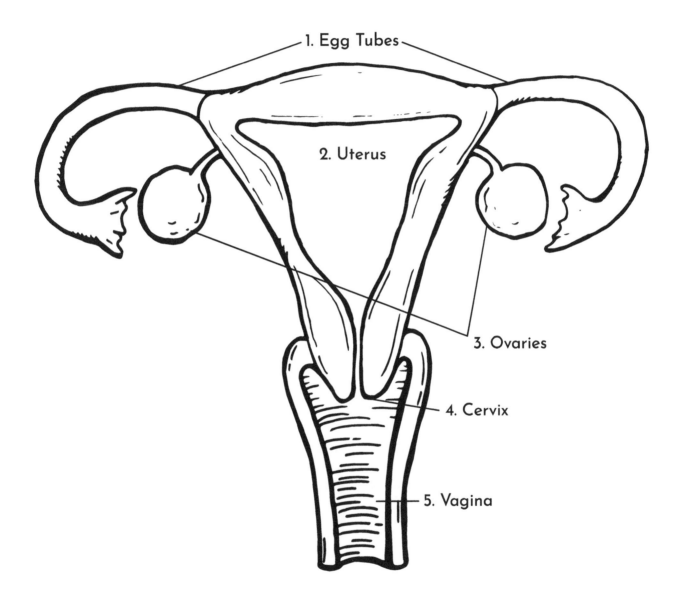

1. Egg Tubes

2. Uterus

3. Ovaries

4. Cervix

5. Vagina

LAYERS OF UTERINE TISSUE

Endometrium

Myometrium

Perimetrium

1. Endometrium

This layer of tissue expires & renews itself cyclically in response to hormonal changes. Endometrium sheds & is released through the cervix during the process of menstruation. What most people refer to as menstrual blood is mostly endometrial tissue. If conception occurs, this tissue serves as a nourishing nest for a fertilized egg to burrow into.

The cyclical shedding of endometrium is a normal, natural, & not an inherently painful process. *Any physical pain with the process ought to be interpreted as the body's communication that something about our health or life circumstances needs transformation & healing.*

2. Myometrium

Myometrium is made of smooth muscles, the same type as our hearts & intestines. The myometrium is responsible for contractions during menstruation & childbirth alike. This powerful part of the uterus is comprised of three separate layers woven cleverly together forming a magical shape shifting basket. During menstruation & pregnancy releases these layers of smooth muscle expand & contract to push the contents of the uterus out through the cervix.

3. Perimetrium

The perimetrium serves as a sort of protective shell or membrane for the endometrial & myometrial layers to do their work inside of. The back surface of the uterus is completely covered by the perimetrium, but the front is only partially enclosed.

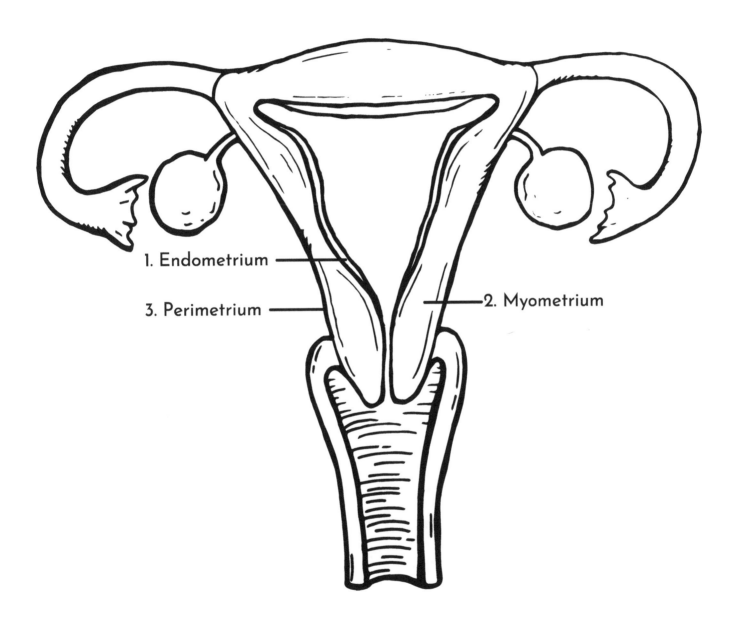

1. Endometrium

3. Perimetrium

2. Myometrium

FIMBRIAE

Fimbriae

Ovary

Eggs

Fimbriae, singular *fimbria*, are the "fringe" or "fingers" at the end of the egg tubes. Before & during the process of ovulation the fimbriae become swollen with blood. The fingers move around the ovary much like sea anemone, creating waves in the fluids of the pelvic cavity. The movement created by their engorgement helps create a "come hither" motion to encourage the egg to enter the tube after its emerges from the ovary.

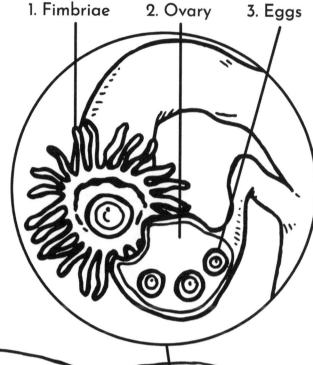

1. Fimbriae   2. Ovary   3. Eggs

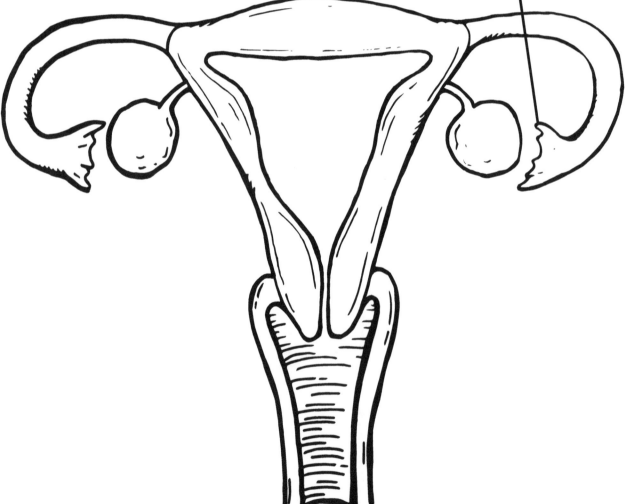

CONNECTIVE TISSUE

The uterus is held by connective tissues that suspend it in the pelvis much like a baby swinging in a hammock. This connective tissue will contract in response to stress, both positive & negative, physical & emotional. It can pull the position of the uterus subtly or dramatically up, down, & from side to side.

In this illustration you can see the special function of two pieces of this connective tissue during sexual arousal. This tissue creates a bridge between the top of the uterus, near where the egg tubes begin, extends over the pubic bone, & attaches to muscles that surround the vaginal opening. As sexual arousal builds this tissue contracts & pulls the uterus forward & up, moving the cervix & womb out of harm's way if there is to be deep penetration in the vagina. During orgasm these muscles spasm causing the uterus to bounce up & down! This movement is thought to assist in potential semen intake, should there be a conveniently located pool of semen in the back of the vagina at the time of orgasm.

These particular pieces of connective tissue are referred to as "round ligaments" in most anatomy texts, simply because the AMAB equivalent is pure ligament. In the AFAB body this tissue is able to perform its unique function due to its smooth muscle core, which is not technically a ligament at all!

Relaxed

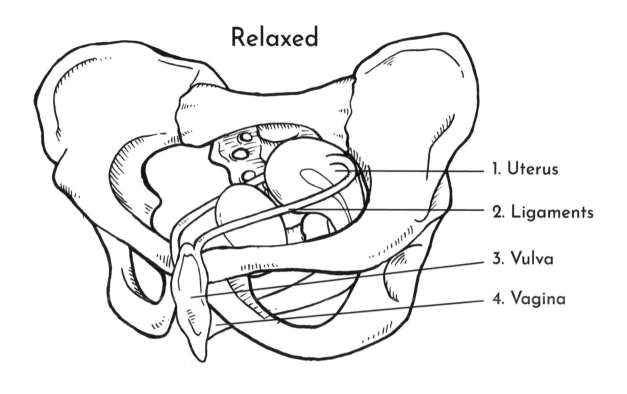

1. Uterus
2. Ligaments
3. Vulva
4. Vagina

Aroused

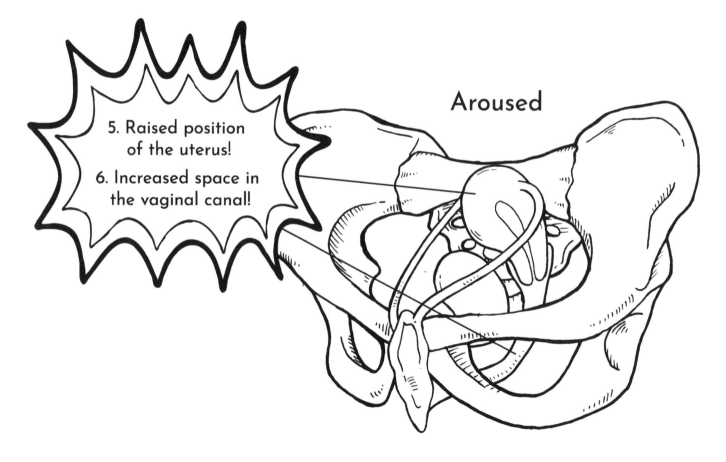

5. Raised position of the uterus!

6. Increased space in the vaginal canal!

Relaxed

- Uterus
- Ligaments
- Vulva
- Vagina

Aroused & Contracted

- Increased space in vaginal canal
- Raised position of uterus

A NOTE ABOUT VAGINAL FLUIDS & SECRETIONS

All vaginal fluids are not created equally! There are many types & each serves a unique important purpose in our body's ecology, & originate in different spots in its geography.

Shockingly, most of what people think are fluids emerging from the vagina are not fluids at all! Technically, menstrual fluids are in fact composed of more tissue than blood. The majority of vaginal sexual arousal fluids are made of substances called *transudate* & *plasma*, & tend to contain a large quantity of skin cells as well. Transudate & plasma originate in the vascular system & get pushed through the vaginal walls during the engorgement process of arousal response. They are present in small amounts in non-aroused vaginas as well to keep the tissues healthy & moist.

Wetness & gooeyness that is not from sexual arousal is often sourced in the cervical glands.

Non-arousal fluids found in or around the vagina may originate from the glands discussed here. All vaginal fluids are hormonally influenced & their properties are subject to change throughout the menstrual cycle & menopause.

GLANDS

Cervical Glands

Paraurethral Glands

Vestibular Glands

1. Cervical Glands

Oddly, for a body part that is in both form & function vital for bringing life into the world, the glands inside the cervix are referred to as "crypts" in medical & academic anatomy terminology. These glands produce fluids throughout our fertility cycle. Cervical fluids play a vital role in fertility, & shift greatly with our hormonal cycles. During the height of the fertile phase of the cycle, which lasts an average of 3-6 days, cervical glands release a sugary alkaline fluid perfect for keeping sperm alive & helping their journey to meet an egg at ovulation. Cervical fluids can be anywhere from glue-ey, sticky, creamy, tacky, to thin, watery, clear, or stretchy. For more information about the meaning & fluctuation of cervical fluids, please see my book "Ovulation Awareness."

2. Paraurethral Glands

The paraurethral glands, also sometimes called "lesser vestibular glands" or by their eponym "Skenes," are located on the top (closer to the pubic mound) wall of the vagina.

The wellspring that the paraurethral glands draw their fluids from contain many tiny tubes like a root system that opens into two main ducts on either side of the urethra. There are as many as 30 tiny ducts, or roots, along the length of the urethra. The function of these glands is very similar to the AMAB prostate gland. An international standard name for this anatomy is "female prostate." These glands are where ejaculate fluid can spout from during heightened sexual arousal or orgasm. The fluid they ejaculate is clear, alkaline, & *not urine*. A small amount of urine may be found in the ejaculate fluid due to the 30 or so tiny roots from this network that live along the urethra itself, but ejaculate fluids do not originate from the bladder.

Whether or not ejaculation takes place, these glands secrete a small amount of mucous to lubricate the vagina through a normal day, with an increased output of fluids during sexual arousal.

3. Vestibular Glands

The eponym for this pair of glands is "Bartholins." The vestibular glands are two pea to grape sized glands on the left & right sides of bottom (closer to the anus) vaginal wall. They are very close to the vaginal opening. This fluid is similar in chemical make up to that secreted by the prostate gland & found in semen. Similar to the Paraurethral glands, the Vestibular glands are regularly secreting small amounts of mucous to help keep tissues healthy & fend off infections, with an increased output of fluids during sexual arousal to improve the lubrication of the vaginal opening.

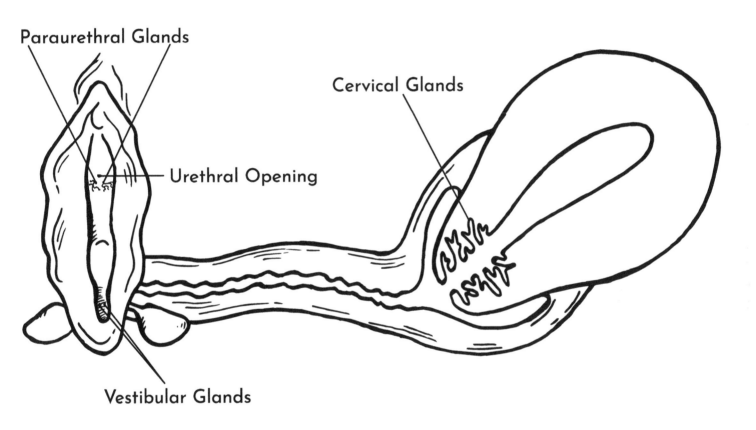

Paraurethral Glands

Cervical Glands

Urethral Opening

Vestibular Glands

Part 2

SEXUAL
ENERGY
ANATOMY

Mapping the Yoniverse ✳ Samantha Zipporah

The modern compartmentalization of mind, body, & spirit is an oppressive illusion.

We are hyper-dimensional beings.

I believe our sexual & reproductive anatomy is one of, if not the most visceral direct dial to the divine we possess as humans.

I am not alone in this belief.

The spiritual & energetic aspects of sexuality & fertility have been revered as sacred for millenia in diverse cultures across the globe. Not only have they been revered, they have been mapped in detail both visually & linguistically. The diagrams, definition, & discussion of the following ancient traditions are reductionist at best. These are rich & diverse lineages & each concept explored has infinite interpretations, rituals & beliefs surrounding them.

I offer them as an invitation for you to explore your own unique experience of energy anatomy. It is my hope that some of these concepts or practices will inspire a felt experience of resonance, reverence, or self awareness for you. As you explore the lineages & traditions of bloodlines that do not belong to you, please do so with respect for the nuanced difference between appropriation & appreciation.

UNIFYING PHILOSOPHIES

Among the diverse lineages discussed here there are many unifying principles, philosophies & beliefs about the purpose & function of our sexual energy. Here are just a few of them:

Sacred sex raises life force from our genitals & pelvis upward to connect us with healing, transcendence, unity, & ecstasy.

Sacred sex seeks to create dynamic balance & exaltation of opposing dynamic creative forces. *These polar dynamics are often described in the west as 'masculine' & 'feminine' but this is not fully accurate.*

Breath is life. Bringing awareness to our breath & moving it through our bodies with visualization, intention, & ritual can create experiences of transcendence & ecstasy.

Our bodies are holy temples within which we can worship & experience the divine.

All spiritual sexual practices can be practiced solo, or with partner(s).

Our natural authentic desires are good. They guide us to manifest & embody our Destiny.

TAOISM & THE MICROCOSMIC ORBIT

Taoism (Daoism) is a religious & philosophical tradition of Chinese origin that emphasizes living in harmony with the Tao, which means the "way," "path," or "principle." The branches of Taoism are diverse & plentiful.

Taoism offers many meditation & breathing exercises that help cultivate sexual vitality & health. Sexual energy is respected as a powerful source of healing & vitality for the whole body & being. Yin & Yang are used to describe polar qualities whose interaction influences the destinies of all things.

One of the most basic visualizations used in Taoist practices, both sexual & non, is circulating energy through The Microcosmic Orbit. Starting at the perineum, using breath & visualization we can move energy up the Yang (or Governor) channel. From the crown of the head, the energy is then channeled down the roof of the mouth through the tongue into the Yin (Functional, or Conception) channel. One can practice breathing through the Microcosmic Orbit solo, or with a partner. This type of breathing can be beneficial with or without sexual arousal or activity. When practiced during sexual activity microcosmic orbit breathing can increase the strength, length, & number of orgasms experienced.

Mantak Chia & Rachel Abram's book "The Multi-Orgasmic Woman" is a great beginner's guide to Taoist sexual practices & philosophy.

> **Governor / Yang Channel** upward energy starting at perineum, up the back, spine, crown, through roof of mouth

> **Functional / Yin / Conception Channel** downward energy from tongue, front, belly, heart, throat

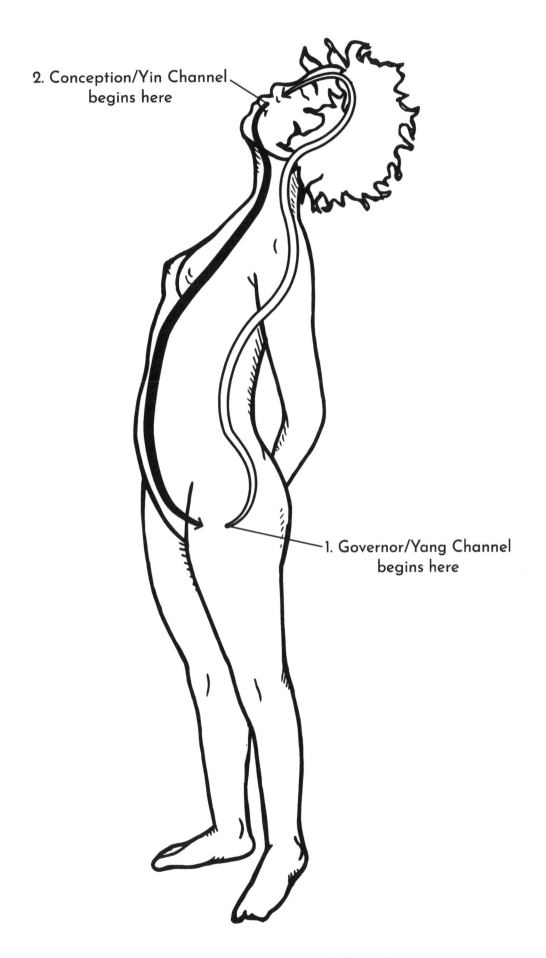

2. Conception/Yin Channel
begins here

1. Governor/Yang Channel
begins here

TANTRA

Tantra's roots can be traced at least 5,000 years back to their origin in India. Tantra is not just a spiritual pursuit, but also socio-political revolt aimed in part at breaking down India's strict caste system, the compartmentalization of mind, body, spirit, & the stigma of pleasure characteristic of most Buddhist & Hindu traditions.

Tantra translates roughly as "The Weaving," & its practice is all about integration & unity. Kundalini & Chakra energies are just two of many concepts in Tantric traditions used to describe our energy anatomy.

Kundalini life force energy, translates as "coiled one" & is personified as a female snake who lives at the base of the spine. Tantric & yogic practices are often meant to help kundalini energy rise to the crown.

Chakra is the Sanskrit for wheel or vortex. Though our sexual nature & energy can reside & thrive in any chakra & move throughout them fluidly, the bottom two are the primary sexual centers. In addition to what is shared here, each chakra has nuanced psycho-spiritual aspects, developmental life stages, zodiac, & many other associations.

Anodea Judith's books "Wheels of Life" & "Eastern Body Western Mind" are my favorite books about Chakras.

"Urban Tantra" by is a great starting point for exploring Tantric sexual practices.

    Root Chakra: *Muladhara*, meaning "root" or "support." Associated with the color red, located at the base of the spine, includes perineum & anus.

    Sacral Chakra: *Svadhisthana*, "sweetness." Associated with the color orange , located at the low belly / womb & ovaries, includes sex organs.

The other chakras are:

    Solar Plexus *Manipura* or "lustrous gem." Associated with the color yellow, located between belly button & sternum, includes digestive & other organs.

    Heart *Anahata* or "unstruck." Associated with the color green, located at the center of the chest, includes body parts of heart, lungs, chest & circulation.

    Throat *Vishudha* or "purification." Associated with the color blue, located centrally at the back of the neck, includes body parts of mouth, throat, & ears.

    Third Eye *Ajna* or to "perceive" to "know." Associated with the color purple, located above & between the eyebrows, includes eyes & pituitary gland.

    Crown *Sahasrara*, or "Thousandfold." Associated with the colors violet, gold, & white, located at the top of the head & includes upper skull, cerebral cortex, & skin.

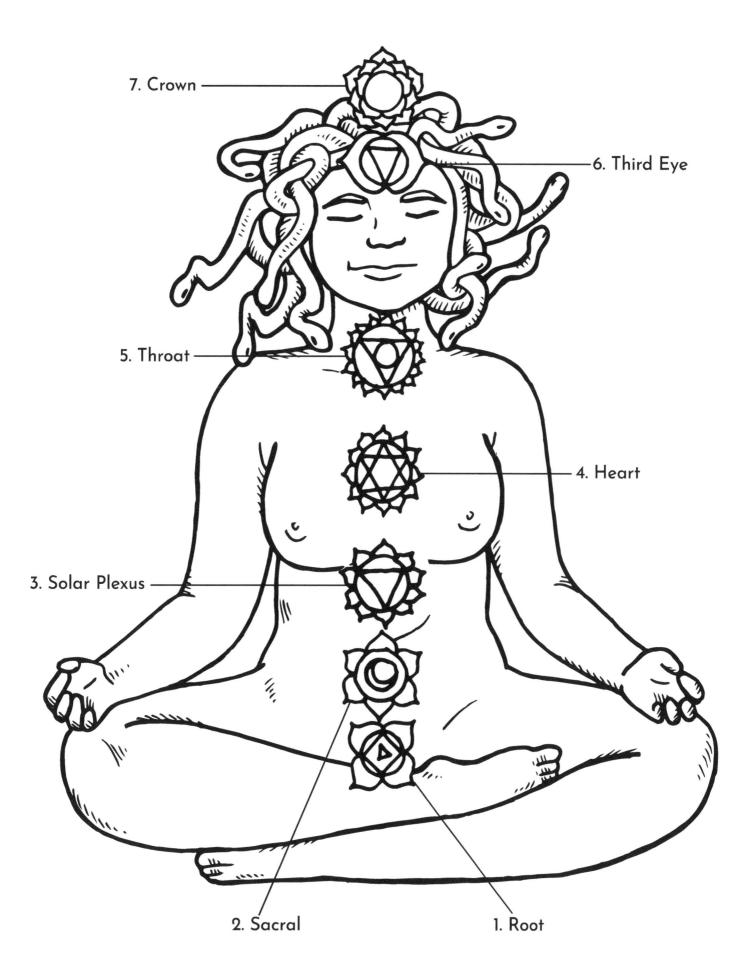

7. Crown

6. Third Eye

5. Throat

4. Heart

3. Solar Plexus

2. Sacral

1. Root

KABBALAH

Kabbalah translates roughly as "The Receiving" & is a form of ancient Jewish mysticism. Some call it the "soul" of the Torah, which is the central holy text in Judaism. While Kabbalah teachings evolved for thousands of years primarily orally, written records can be dated to the 13th century northern Israel, from the city of Zefat.

The Tree of Life is a central symbol in Kabbalah. Much like the chakras in Tantric traditions, the Tree of Life has energy centers, or sephirot, that correlate with body parts & psycho-spiritual qualities. Even though it is commonly pictured at the feet of the body, **Malkut** is the sephirot most associated with sexual energy. Similar to chakras, a flow of energy between all sephirot is necessary for health in any one sephirot. The body is viewed as a mystical bridge from the mundane physical world to the divine spiritual world. We must fully embrace & embody our spirits to reach unity & bliss.

Divine Crown *Keter*

Wisdom *Hokhmah*

Understanding *Binah*

Mercy *Hesed*

Justice *Din*

Beauty *Tif'eret*

Eternity *Nezah*

Glory *Hod*

Foundation *Yesod*

Queendom *Shechinah*

Soul Consciousness Levels

In addition to the sephirot, Kabbalah further describes the nature of human spirit & consciousness in five levels. **Nefesh** is the soul level associated with **Malkut** & primal sexual energy. There is a Kabbalistic saying "Nefesh is in the blood." We engage with Nefesh soul level with embodied sexuality, menstruation & pregnancy releases of all kinds.

Yechida *unity*, bliss, transcendence, infinite

Chaya *life* wisdom body, discernment free of ego

Neshama *breath*, intellectual / mental body, stories, thoughts, understanding

Ruach *wind*, emotional, heart, & astral body

Nefesh *living* / animal soul, physical, animal, primal sexual body & desires

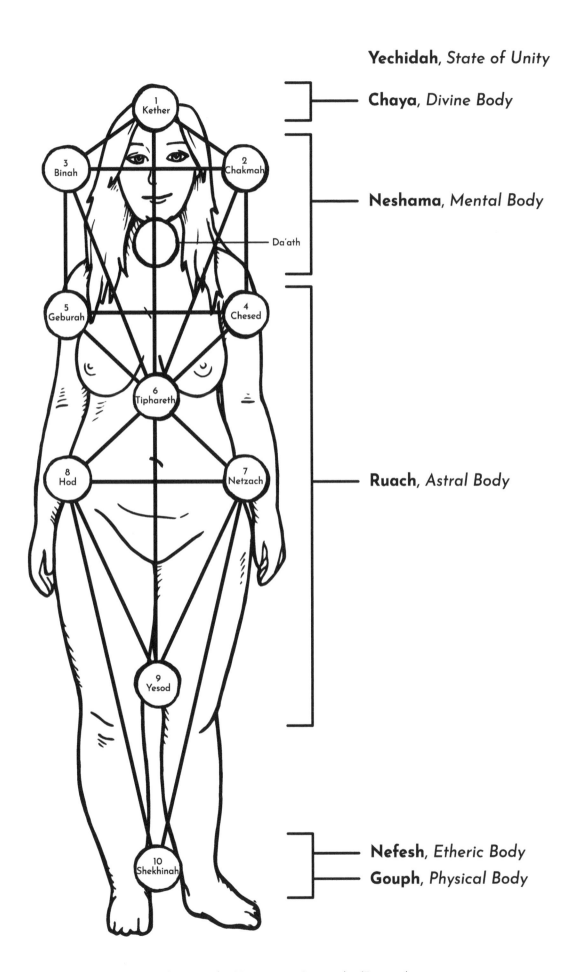

Yechidah, *State of Unity*

Chaya, *Divine Body*

Neshama, *Mental Body*

Ruach, *Astral Body*

Nefesh, *Etheric Body*

Gouph, *Physical Body*

1 Kether

3 Binah

2 Chakmah

Da'ath

5 Geburah

4 Chesed

6 Tiphareth

8 Hod

7 Netzach

9 Yesod

10 Shekhinah

The body as a bridge from the mundane to the heavenly realms

REFERENCES

Carrellas, Barbara, and Annie Sprinkle. *Urban Tantra: Sacred Sex for the Twenty-first Century.* California, NY: Ten Speed Press, 2017.

Chia, Mantak, and Rachel Carlton. Abrams. *The Multi-orgasmic Woman: Sexual Secrets Every Woman Should Know.* New York, NY: HarperOne, 2009.

Constant, C. R., Cecilia Brassett, and Michelle Spear. *The Anatomy Coloring Book.* London, UK: New Holland Publishers, 2010.

Firestone, Rabbi Tirzah. *The Woman's Kabbalah: Ecstatic Jewish Practices for Women.* 2000.

Gage, Suzann, Sylvia Morales, and Katharina Allers. *A New View of a Womans Body: A Fully Illustrated Guide.* Los Angeles: Feminist Health Press, 1995.

Kempton, Sally. *Awakening Shakti: The Transformative Power of the Goddesses of Yoga.* Mumbai: Jaico Publishing House, 2015.

Kerner, Ian. *She Comes First: The Thinking Mans Guide to Pleasuring a Woman.* William Morrow Company, 2010.

Nagoski, Emily PH. D. *Come as You Are: The Surprising New Science That Will Transform Your Sex Life.* New York: Simon & Schuster, 2015.

Northrup, Christiane. *Womens Bodies Womens Wisdom: Creating Physical and Emotional Health and Healing.* New York: Bantam Books, 2002.

Winston, Sheri. *Womens Anatomy of Arousal: Secret Maps to Buried Pleasure.* Kingston, NY: Mango Garden, 2010.

ABOUT THE AUTHOR

Samantha Zipporah is a fertility & sexuality educator, activist, & advocate. She teaches body literacy & walks a path of service to womb sovereignty. She believes the mind, body, & spirit connection deserve reverence & respect. Friends have joked that her business tagline should be, "If anything's going in or out of a cervix, call Sam.

A former birth doula whose roots of study can be found in traditional midwifery "womb to tomb" style care, Sam provides counsel for a diverse array of fertility, sexuality, & pregnancy experiences. Her approach is grounded in a solid understanding of biochemistry & biology, & nourished by playfulness, sass, & reverent spirituality.

To learn more about Sam & her work please visit her at www.samanthazipporah.com & follow her on social media.

ABOUT THE ILLUSTRATOR

Casandra Johns is an herbalist, artist, designer, & mama. She wears a lot of hats & loves to stay busy through collaborative creative endeavors. If it has to do with books, plants, or community, you've captured her interest. Residing in the Pacific Northwest on Kalapuya land, Casandra spends her days studying, tending her herb garden, raising her daughter, & designing beautiful things. She works with Gods & Radicals, a pagan anarchist press, & started House of Hands, a small press-now-turned-design studio. To find her work or collaborate, visit www.houseofhands.net or follow her on Instagram @house.of.hands.

INDEX

A

Anus 10, 12, 13

B

Bartholins 28

Binah 36, 37

C

cervical glands 27, 28, 29

cervix 19, 20, 21, 22, 25, 28, 40

Chakmah 37

chakra 34

Chaya 36, 37

Chesed 37

clitoral head 10, 11, 13, 16, 17, 18

clitoral hood 10, 11, 13

clitoral legs 16, 17, 18

clitoral shaft 10, 11, 13, 16, 17, 18

clitoris 10, 11, 12

Conception Channel 32, 33

connective tissue 25

Crown Sahasrara, 32, 34, 35

crypts 28

D

Da'ath 37

Din 36

E

eggs 20, 24

egg tubes 19, 20, 21

endometrium 22, 23

F

fertility cycle 28

fimbria 24

fimbriae 24

fluid 11, 27, 28

G

Geburah 37

gland 11, 27, 28

Gouph 37

Governor Channel 32, 33

H

Heart Chakra 34, 35

Hesed 36

Hod 36, 37

Hokhmah 36

I

inner lips 10, 11, 13

internal clitoris 16

introitus 11

K

Kabbalah 36

Keter 36, 37

kundalini 34

L

labia majora 10

labia minora 10

ligament 25, 26, 27

M

Malkut 36

menstrual cycle 27

microcosmic orbit 32

mons venus 11

myometrium 22, 23

N

Nefesh 36, 37

Neshama 36, 37

Nezah 36, 37

O

outer lips 10, 13

ovaries 19, 20, 21

P

paraurethral glands 28, 29

perimetrium 22, 23

perineum 10, 12, 13, 32

pubic mound 10, 11, 13

R

Root Chakra 34, 35

Ruach 36, 37

rugea 14

S

Sacral Chakra 34, 35

Shechinah 36, 37

Skenes 28

Solar Plexus 34, 35

T

Tantra 34

Taoism 32

Third Eye 34, 35

Throat Chakra 32, 34, 35

Tif'eret 36, 37

Tree of Life 36

U

urethra 11, 12, 28

urethral opening 10, 13, 29

uterus 19, 21, 25, 26, 27

V

Vagina 11, 12, 19, 21, 26, 27, 28

vaginal canal 27

vaginal fluid 27

vaginal opening 10, 11, 13, 28

vaginal tissue 14

vaginal wall 19, 27, 28

vestibular bulbs 16, 17, 18

vestibular glands 28, 29

vestibule 10, 11,1 3

vulva 8, 10, 12, 26, 27

W

womb 8, 20, 25, 34, 40

Y

Yang 32, 33

Yechida 36, 37

Yesod 36, 37

Yin 32, 33

yoni 8